Time Pieces

for
E flat Saxophone

Music through the Ages in Two Volumes

Volume 2

Selected and arranged by
Ian Denley

The Associated Board of
the Royal Schools of Music

CONTENTS

Time Pieces for E flat Saxophone

Volume 2

for Sharon

1692 **Rondeau** and
Dance for the Haymakers
from *The Fairy Queen*

Henry Purcell
(1659–1695)

RONDEAU
Allegretto ♩ = *c.*100

Fine

AB 2771

D.C. al Fine

DANCE FOR THE HAYMAKERS

Allegro con spirito ♩ = 144–152

1729 Sinfonia

from Cantata No. 156, BWV 156

Johann Sebastian Bach
(1685–1750)

1773 Menuetto e Trio

from Symphony No. 25, K. 183

Wolfgang Amadeus Mozart
(1756–1791)

TRIO

Fine

Menuetto D.C. al Fine

1801 Allegro molto

from Serenade Op. 25

Ludwig van Beethoven
(1770–1827)

CODA

D.C. al Coda

1872 Orchestral solo

from *L'arlésienne*, Suite I

Georges Bizet
(1838–1875)

1888 Two Little Pearls

Antonín Dvořák
(1841–1904)

1. In a Ring!

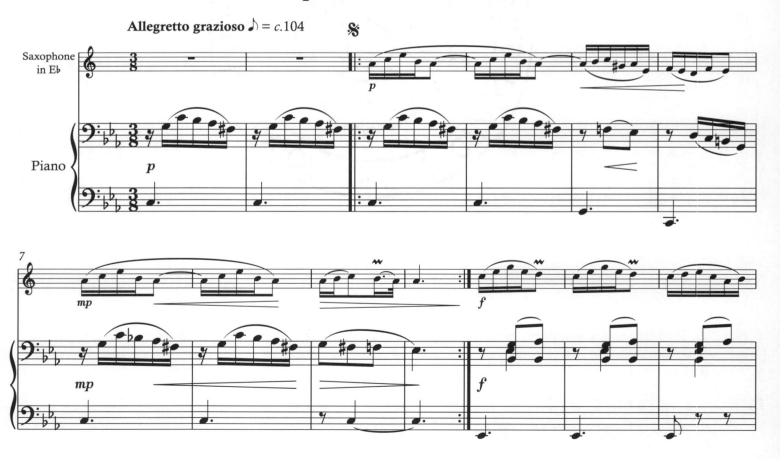

2. Grandpa Dances with Grandma

Fine

D.S. al Fine

1900 Entry of the Gladiators

Op. 68

Julius Fučik
(1872–1916)

AB 2771

Time Pieces for E flat Saxophone
Volume 2

for Sharon

1692 **Rondeau** and
Dance for the Haymakers
from *The Fairy Queen*

Henry Purcell
(1659–1695)

RONDEAU

AB 2771

DANCE FOR THE HAYMAKERS

1729 Sinfonia
from Cantata No. 156, BWV 156

Johann Sebastian Bach
(1685–1750)

1773 Menuetto e Trio

from Symphony No. 25, K. 183

Wolfgang Amadeus Mozart
(1756–1791)

MENUETTO

Allegro ♩ = 120–126

Menuetto D.C. al Fine

1801 Allegro molto

from Serenade Op. 25

Ludwig van Beethoven
(1770–1827)

1872 Orchestral solo

from *L'arlésienne*, Suite I

Georges Bizet
(1838–1875)

1888 Two Little Pearls

Antonín Dvořák
(1841–1904)

1. In a Ring!

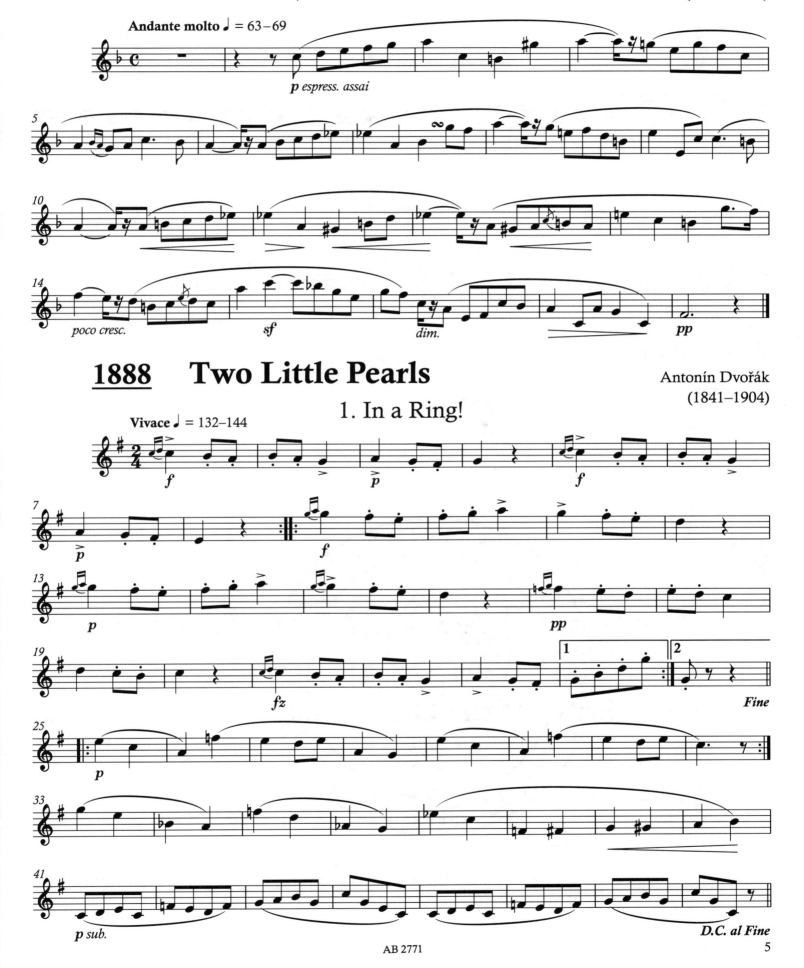

2. Grandpa Dances with Grandma

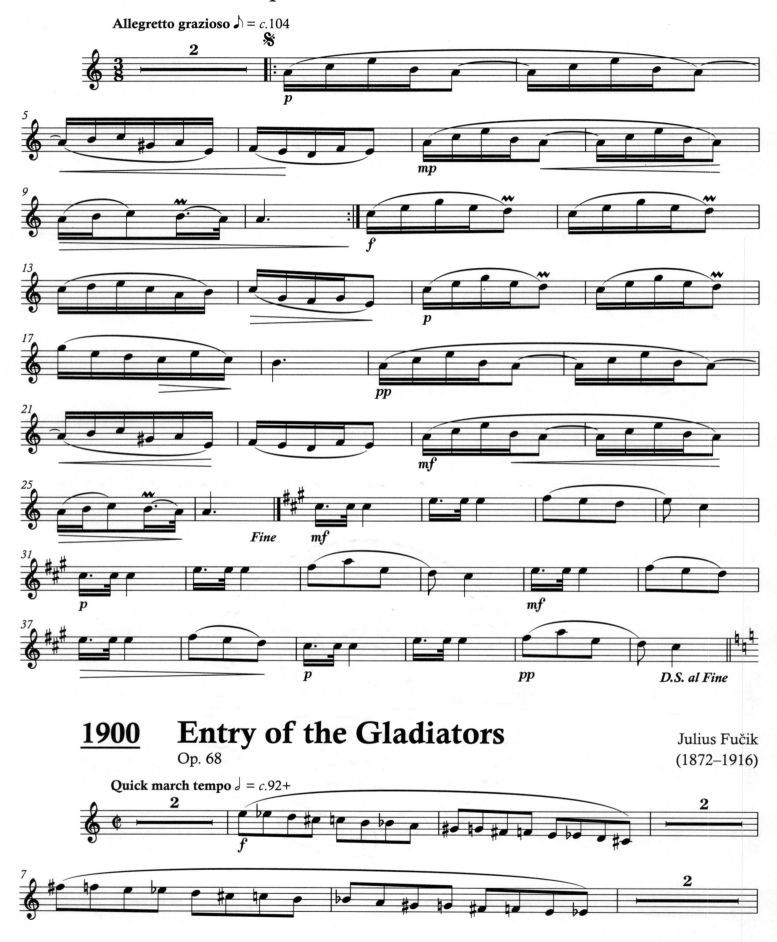

1900 **Entry of the Gladiators**

Op. 68

Julius Fučik
(1872–1916)

AB 2771

1905 Pavane pour une infante défunte

Maurice Ravel
(1875–1937)

1928 Tango-Ballade

from *The Threepenny Opera*

Kurt Weill
(1900–1950)

Tango-tempo ♩ = 60–69

1945   Prelude No. 2
from *Six Preludes*, Op. 23

Lennox Berkeley
(1903–1989)

1945   Clockwork Doll
from *Six Children's Pieces*, Op. 69

Dmitry Shostakovich
(1906–1975)

1953 March
from *Three Youthful Pieces*

Witold Lutosławski
(1913–1994)

Allegro ♩ = 108–112

2000 New Age Tango

John McLeod
(b. 1934)

Printed in England by Caligraving Ltd, Thetford, Norfolk

Music origination by
Barnes Music Engraving Ltd, East Sussex

AB 2771

7:02

1905 Pavane pour une infante défunte

Maurice Ravel
(1875–1937)

AB 2771

Tango-Ballade

1928 from *The Threepenny Opera*

Kurt Weill
(1900–1950)

1945 Prelude No. 2

from *Six Preludes*, Op. 23

Lennox Berkeley

(1903–1989)

1945 Clockwork Doll

from *Six Children's Pieces*, Op. 69

Dmitry Shostakovich
(1906–1975)

1953 March

from *Three Youthful Pieces*

Witold Lutosławski
(1913–1994)

2000 New Age Tango

John McLeod
(b. 1934)

AB 2771

poco rit.

a tempo

rit.

Music origination by
Barnes Music Engraving Ltd, East Sussex
Printed in England by Caligraving Ltd, Thetford, Norfolk

AB 2771
7:02